Kisses From Dolce

A Book for Children About Trusting and Telling

Written and Illustrated

By

Susan Komisar Hausman

In Gratitude...

Words alone cannot adequately express my thanks to those who have encouraged me, believed in me, listened to me and were my backbone when I struggled. Without you, there would be no "Kisses From Dolce."

Jon, Jacqueline, Mom, Dad, Dr. Carrie Rubin, Susan Mason, Lauren Oltarsh, Susan Brooks, Marilyn Rabinovitz, Craig Hoffman, Carlie Centrella, Marcy Bass, Jackie Madwed, Gail Beer, David Rabinovitz, Jodi Greene, David Crosby, Amy Pransky, Lila Grossman, Lisa Lust, Cynthia Zabin, Susan Panisch, Kathi Greenfield, Lynn Flaster Paul, Ruby Barry, Alice Madwed, Ruth Madwed and Dr. Elayne S. Daniels.

To Joanne Sonick, of blessed memory, who took the time, years ago, in her last, precious days, to remind me that if I wanted to get something done, I needed to take charge and do it myself. I heard you Joanne.

Finally...

I have learned on this journey that inspiration can come from the most unexpected places. And, so, to an adorable 4-legged boy who, other than one little slurp, had absolutely no interest in me; to you, the original "Signore Dolce," and your 2-legged daddy, I say, "Grazie."

In memory of my father, Harold
In honor of my daughter, Jacqueline

My past and my future, forever intertwined
I love you both

Just down the street,
In a place not too far,
There is a kids' daycare
Called Once Upon a Star.

With toys, books and games
In each of its spaces,
Most every day
There are many happy faces!

Here come the kids...

Jackie and Ali,
Sophia and Josh,
Samantha-Rebecca
(she dresses so posh!)
Heidi and Aimee and cute little Ben,
Izzy and Carlos and don't forget Jenn!
Sara and Sam,
And dear little Maggie,
That's the whole gang....

Hey, what's in the Baggie?™

These look like treats,
Could they be for a doggie?
The last pet we had here
Was green Mr. Froggie!

4

These look like they might be
Meant for a hound.
"Indeed," said Miss Carrie,
"Just look around."
And there, in the corner,
For everyone to see,
Sleeping so soundly...

Was that little IG!

"Italian Greyhound!"
shouted Sophia,
"I know that is true!
My Papa and Nona,
They have one too!"

"His name is Dolce,
That's Italian for 'sweet'.
Having him here
Is a wonderful treat!
We'll watch him grow,
Soon he will play,
Then he can spend
Lots of the day."

And grow Dolce did,
Just like the rest of the kids.
He played really hard,
Sometimes he'd get in the lids!
One time they found him
On top of the books,
Chewing the hats
Off the metal coat hooks!
He's often so silly,
That little IG,
But the kids they just love him,
He's "dolce" as could be!!

8

He loves them, too!
When they sit on their knees,
He sticks his nose in their hair
And checks them for fleas!
But he seems just so stingy
When it comes to giving kisses.
He gives just one slurp!
"More, more" are their wishes!

Especially Sophia,
She just loves to snuggle,
Sometimes he'll give her a lick
And then she'll just chuckle!

But one day,
Not too long after vacation,
Sophia came in,
But with much hesitation.
She wouldn't talk with the kids,
Or even Miss Carrie.
Even little Dolce
Couldn't get Sophia to tarry.

She didn't want to be bothered,
And just played with some dishes,
Pushing Dolce away
When he tried to give her kisses.

"Yuck," she had said,
"I don't want to be touched."

"OK, Sophia...
We won't bother you much."

Smart Miss Carrie knew
little Sophia was sad,
So she gave her extra space
And some time to be mad.

"If you ever want to talk,
You can share with me.
You deserve to feel safe
And happy as can be.
You can tell me anything
You have on your mind.
Whatever you're feeling,
It's perfectly fine."

Sophia thought and thought for a while,
Then went to Miss Carrie,
Who gave her a smile.

In Miss Carrie's ear she whispered...

"I'm scared and I'm sad.
Someone's been touching me
And it makes me feel bad.
I want it to stop,
To go far away."

"I can help you, Sophia,
Right now, today."

"You've done nothing wrong,
You are good and you are brave.

Your body is private,
It belongs just to you.
You have the right to say no,
To anyone, yes, you do."

Miss Carrie made some phone calls
To people she knew
Who could help make things better,
Thank goodness! Phew!

It took a little while,
Some days and some weeks,
But, soon, there was that glow again
In Sophia's cheeks!

Then she was smiling and playing again,
With her friends at the daycare,
And her little hound friend.

Now when Dolce comes running through the door,
Just like she did so often before,
Sophia makes a beeline right over to that pooch,
Runs up and hugs him and gives HIM a smooch!

Dolce's so happy and the kids all delighted,
To see Sophia happy, laughing and excited!
The next thing you know,
Mr. Dolce, that hound,
Jumps up in her arms,
Sophia's cheek he has found!
And with her permission,
He gives her a lick, just to play!

'Cause now, especially to Sophia,
Nothing's as nice as kisses from Dolce!

Questions adult readers might want to consider with the children:

Sophia trusted Miss Carrie enough to ask for her help. Can you think of people in your life who can help you if you need it?

How do people show they care about you or how they like you? What ways do you show people you like them?

What kind of touching is ok? When? By whom?

When is it ok to keep secrets? When isn't it?

Special thanks to Dr. Elayne S. Daniels, Dr. Carrie J. Rubin and Marilyn Rabinovitz for their contributions to this page.

Resources

For educators and other mandated reporters: know what your state requires if you are suspicious about abuse.

For parents: don't panic... kids can be additionally traumatized by adults' reactions...call your local authorities at 911 for immediate assistance.

The numbers below can help if you don't know where to turn. Each can provide referrals to local centers for help.

Darkness to Light's National Helpline Network
1-866-FOR-LIGHT (1-866-367-5444)
www.DarknessToLight.org

National Sexual Assault Hotline at 1.800.656.HOPE

Childhelp USA National Child Abuse Hotline
1-800-422-4453
1-800-4-A-CHILD
www.childhelpusa.org

Stop It Now
1-888-PREVENT
www.stopitnow.org

Mention of the above organizations in no way implies their endorsement of this book.

ISBN: 978-1-4251-8138-3 (sc)

 www.trafford.com

North America & international
toll-free: 1 888 232 4444 (USA & Canada)
fax: 812 355 4082

Made in the USA
San Bernardino, CA
08 September 2018